PHONICS

with
Oscar Octopus

Stage 5

AGES 4-7

Contents

y y y y y y y y y y y y y y y y y y y y y

Join the letters to make the word.

Read the word. Hear the letter sounds.

r a i n y

rain**y**

Join the letters to make the words.

l a d y　　**b a b y**　　**p o n y**

_____　　_____　　_____

Label the pictures correctly.

_____　　_____　　_____

Join the letters to make the words and write them below. Draw a picture in the boxes.

_____　　_____　　_____

l o r r y　　**l o l l y**　　**p u p p y**

2

When 'y' comes at the end of some words it is sometimes pronounced like 'ee' (as in Humpty Dumpty).

y y y y y y y y y y y y y y y y y y y y y y y y

Join up the pairs of rhyming words.

Write the words.

silly

funny

carry

hurry

tummy

sorry

dotty

tubby

saggy

sunny

hilly

mummy

curry

marry

spotty

baggy

lorry

grubby

silly   hilly

PARENT'S TIPS
After joining up the pairs of rhyming words, see how many others you can think of. Make up rhymes with some of the words.

3

Join the letters to make the word.

Read the word. Hear the letter sounds.

p u sh

p**u**sh

Join the letters to make the words.

f **u** ll   p **u** t   p **u** sh

_____   _____   _____

Label the pictures correctly.

_____   _____   _____

Join the letters to make the words and write them below. Draw a picture in the boxes.

_____   _____   _____

b **u** sh   p **u** ll   b **u** ll

4

PARENT'S TIPS

Your child will remember the sound of 'u' in these words with the rhyme 'never pull or push a bull in a bush!'.

Use the words in the box below to answer the crossword.

full   pull   bull
bush   push   put

across

1 _____ your toys away in the cupboard.
3 The opposite of empty.
4 Like a small tree.

down

1 The opposite of push.
2 The opposite of pull.
4 A farm animal.

PARENT'S TIPS   Help your child to read all the 'u' words in the box before attempting to do the crossword.

5

Join the letters to make the word.

Read the word. Hear the letter sounds.

b **oo** k

b**oo**k

Join the letters to make the words.

w **oo** d   h **oo** d   f **oo** t

_____   _____   _____

Label the pictures correctly.

_____   _____   _____

Join the letters to make the words and write them below. Draw a picture in the boxes.

_____   _____   _____

h **oo** k   c **oo** k   c r **oo** k

PARENT'S TIPS

Whenever the letters 'oo' come together they make one sound. Look back at page 4 and ask your child what they notice about the 'oo' and 'u' sounds. (They sound the same.)

- Play the game with a partner.
- You need a counter each and a coin.
- Take it in turns to spin the coin.
- Tails = move one space. Heads = move two spaces.
- Read the word you land on each time.
- If you can't read the word, miss a turn.
- The first person to reach the end is the winner.

Look out for the wolf!

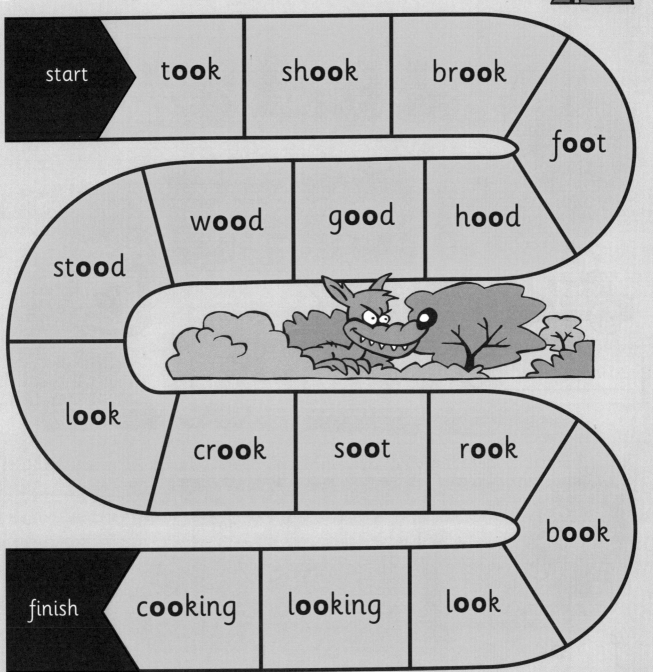

start | took | shook | brook | foot
wood | good | hood
stood | look
crook | soot | rook | book
finish | cooking | looking | look

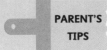

PARENT'S TIPS   Have a practice run first and help your child build and read each word before playing the actual game.

Join the letters to make the word.

Read the word. Hear the letter sounds.

c ar

c**ar**

Join the letters to make the words.

s t **ar**

j **ar**

c **ar** t

_____   _____   _____

Label the pictures correctly.

_____   _____   _____

Join the letters to make the words and write them below. Draw a picture in the boxes.

f **ar** m

sh **ar** k

s c **ar** f

8

PARENT'S TIPS

Whenever the letters 'ar' come together they make one sound. Encourage your child to finger trace the 'ar' letters whilst saying the sound aloud.

Fill in the missing **ar** in each gap on my c**ar**d.

Dear T_____a

Please come to my p_____ty on M_____ch 5th.

It st_____ts at 4 o'clock sh_____p. It goes on until it's

d_____k and the st_____s come out!

If it's fine it will be in the g_____den.

If it rains it will be in the b_____n.

Dress sm_____tly!

    From

        M_____k.

Please send your reply to Cherry Tree F_____m.

Write all the **ar** words here.

PARENT'S TIPS

Help your child read the birthday card after completing it.

a a a a a a a a a a a a a a a a a a a a a a a a a a a

Join the letters to make the word.

Read the word. Hear the letter sounds.

r a f t

r**a**ft

Join the letters to make the words.

f a s t   g l a ss   g r a ss

_____   _____   _____

Label the pictures correctly.

_____   _____   _____

Join the letters to make the words and write them below. Draw a picture in the boxes.

p a th   b a th   m a s k

10

PARENT'S TIPS — In some words 'a' is sometimes pronounced like 'ar', as in 'glass' (although there may be regional variations in this).

Follow each p**a**th with your pencil. Which word does each p**a**th lead to? Fill in the answers at the bottom.

Path A

Path B

Path C

Path D

Path E

Path F

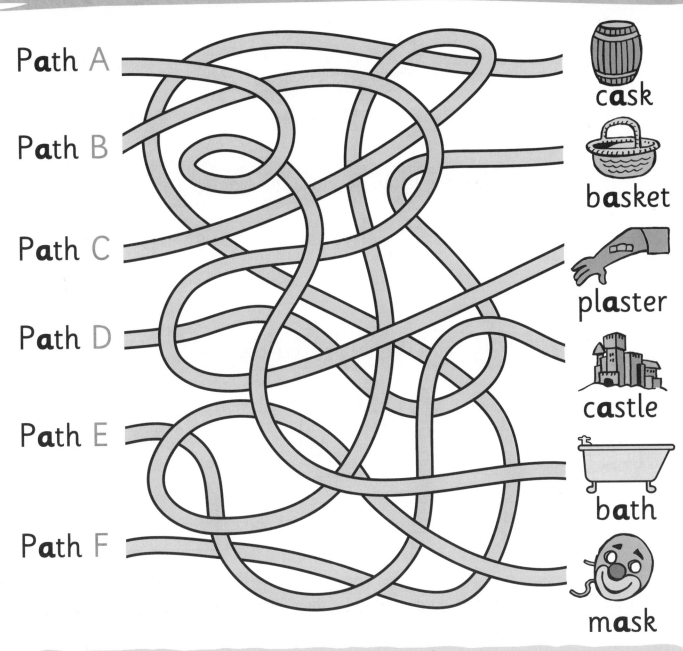

c**a**sk

b**a**sket

pl**a**ster

c**a**stle

b**a**th

m**a**sk

Path A → _____

Path B → _____

Path C → _____

Path D → _____

Path E → _____

Path F → _____

PARENT'S TIPS — Have fun guessing which label goes to which picture before tracing the twisty lines to find out.

11

Join the letters to make the word.

Read the word. Hear the letter sounds.

oi + l

oil

Join the letters to make the words.

b + oi + l   c + oi + l   s p + oi + l

_____   _____   _____

Label the pictures correctly.

_____   _____   _____

Join the letters to make the words and write them below. Draw a picture in the boxes.

_____   _____   _____

j + oi + n   c + oi + n   p + oi + n t

12

PARENT'S TIPS

Explain that when 'oi' come together in a word they make one sound.

Join the meanings to the words.

to lift	boil
damp	coin
to fix together	hoist
to ruin	join
you speak with it	point
to be happy	spoil
money	moist
to cook in water	voice
a sharp end	rejoice

PARENT'S TIPS — Help your child to read the definitions before attempting to join them up to the correct 'oi' words.

Join the letters to make the word.

Read the word. Hear the letter sounds.

r oy a l

royal

Join the letters to make the words.

j oy   e n j oy   oy s t er

_____   _____   _____

Label the pictures correctly.

_____   _____   _____

Join the letters to make the words and write them below. Draw a picture in the boxes.

_____   _____   _____

b oy   t oy   a n n oy

PARENT'S TIPS

Look back at page 12 and ask your child what they notice about the 'oi' and 'oy' sounds. (They sound the same – but 'oi' always comes within a word whereas 'oy' sometimes comes at the end of a word.)

Complete each **oy** word on the fish. Write the **oy** words in the grid.

t oy

b___

enj____

destr____

ann____

empl____

j___ful

____ster

r___al

v___age

t	o		y
	o		y
	o		y
		o	y
	o	y	
		o	y
	o	y	
o	y		
	o	y	
			o	y

Join the letters to make the word.

Read the word. Hear the letter sounds.

ow l

ow l

Join the letters to make the words.

c **ow**

c r **ow** n

g **ow** n

Label the pictures correctly.

Join the letters to make the words and write them below. Draw a picture in the boxes.

t **ow** n

t **ow** er

c r **ow** d

16

PARENT'S TIPS

Explain that when 'ow' come together in a word they make one sound.

Float each **ow** to a landing platform. Write the **ow** word it makes.

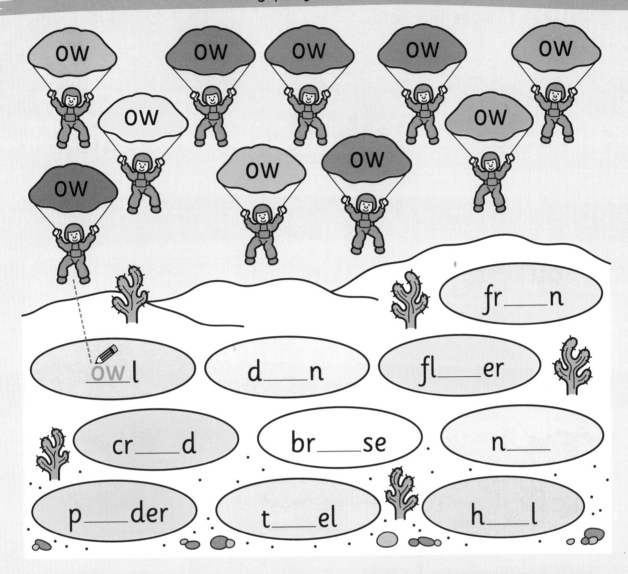

OW OW OW OW OW
OW OW OW OW

fr___n

<u>ow</u> l   d___n   fl___er

cr___d   br___se   n___

p___der   t___el   h___l

Write the **ow** words above with …

… 3 letters

… 4 letters

… 5 letters

… 6 letters

Join the letters to make the word.

Read the word. Hear the letter sounds.

c **ou** n t

co**u**nt

Join the letters to make the words.

sh **ou** t   m **ou** th   c l **ou** d

_____   _____   _____

Label the pictures correctly.

_____   _____   _____

Join the letters to make the words and write them below. Draw a picture in the boxes.

f **ou** n d   p **ou** n d   r **ou** n d

18

PARENT'S TIPS   Look back at page 16 and ask your child what they notice about the 'ow' and 'ou' sounds. (They sound the same – but 'ou' always comes within a word whereas 'ow' often comes at the end of a word.)

Find the **ou** words in the cloud.

Finish the words below using the **ou** words you fo**u**nd in the cl**ou**d.

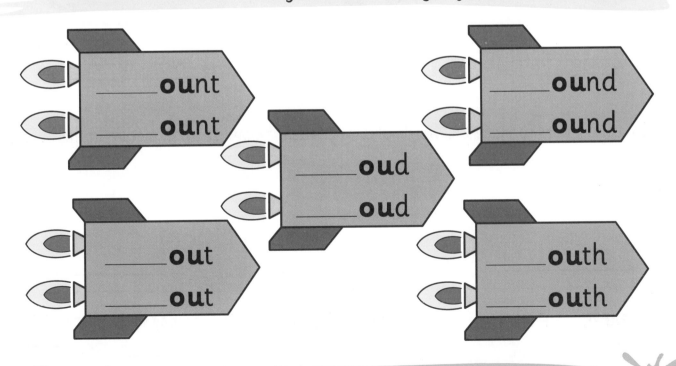

PARENT'S TIPS — Ask your child to be a 'word detective' and look for the 'ou' words 'hiding' on the page. Developing a good eye for words is an important element of reading and spelling.

19

Join the letters to make the word.

Read the word. Hear the letter sounds.

wh isper

whisper

Join the letters to make the words.

wh ip

wh isk

wh eat

_____   _____   _____

Label the pictures correctly.

_____   _____   _____

Join the letters to make the words and write them below. Draw a picture in the boxes.

_____   _____   _____

wh eel

wh ale

wh ack

20

Whenever the letters 'wh' come together in a word they make one sound. Notice how the 'h' remains silent in each word.

Use the words in the box below to answer the crossword.

wheels
whale

whisk
whiskers

whirl
whisper

wheat
white

across

1 To spin round.
2 Cats have these on their faces.
3 You use this in the kitchen.
5 You find this animal in the sea.
6 The colour of snow.

down

1 A car has four of these.
2 To speak quietly.
4 Bread is made of this.

PARENT'S TIPS — Help your child to read all the 'wh' words in the box before attempting to do the crossword.

Join the letters to make the word.

Read the word. Hear the letter sounds.

ph oto

photo

Join the letters to make the words.

dol **ph** in   al **ph** abet   **ph** antom

_____   _____   _____

Label the pictures correctly.

abcdefghi
jklmnopqr
stuvwxyz

_____   _____   _____

Join the letters to make the words and write them below. Draw a picture in the boxes.

_____   _____   _____

ph one   ele **ph** ant   **ph** otogra **ph**

PARENT'S TIPS

Ask your child to trace the letters 'ph' in the air with their fingers, saying 'Phew!' as they do so to remind them that 'ph' makes a 'f' sound in words.

ph ph ph ph ph ph ph ph ph ph ph

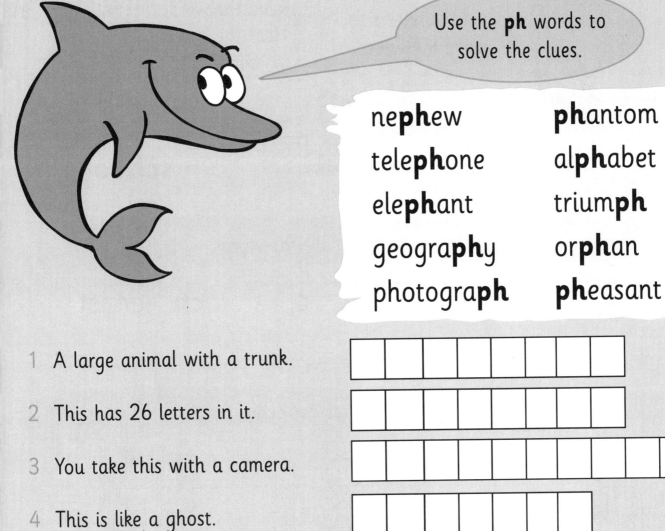

Use the **ph** words to solve the clues.

ne**ph**ew   **ph**antom
tele**ph**one   al**ph**abet
ele**ph**ant   trium**ph**
geogra**ph**y   or**ph**an
photogra**ph**   **ph**easant

1 A large animal with a trunk.

2 This has 26 letters in it.

3 You take this with a camera.

4 This is like a ghost.

5 Lessons about other countries.

6 You can speak to people who are far away with this.

7 A sort of bird.

8 When you win.

9 A child without any parents.

10 A male relative.

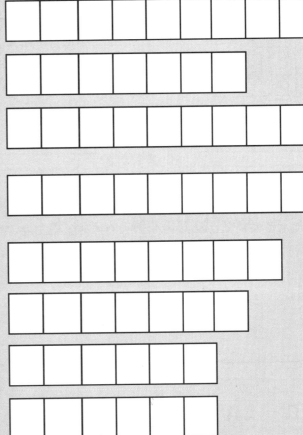

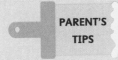

PARENT'S TIPS   Help your child to read all the 'ph' words in the box before attempting to match each word with its meaning.

23

Join the letters to make the word.

Read the word. Hear the letter sounds.

s | ch | oo | l

school

Join the letters to make the words.

ch | oir

e | ch | o

ch | emist

_____ | _____ | _____

Label the pictures correctly.

_____ | _____ | _____

Join the letters to make the words and write them below. Draw a picture in the boxes.

an **ch** or | stoma **ch** | s **ch** oolboy

Trace over the waves in pencil.
Drop a **ch** an**ch**or into each word when you read it.

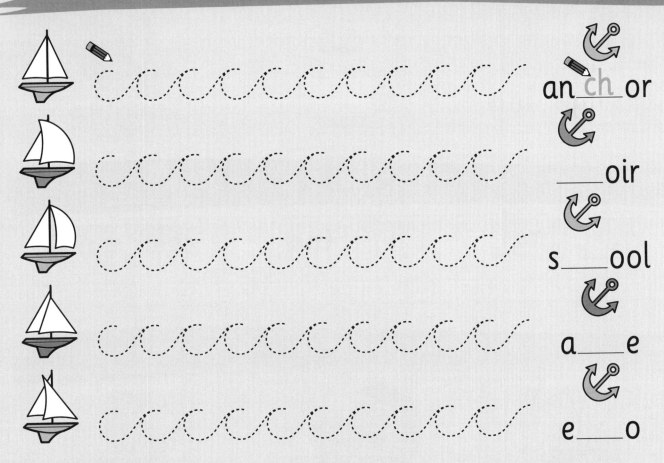

an_ch_or

___oir

s___ool

a___e

e___o

Use the correct word in each sentence.

1 A _____ is a group who sing.

2 An _____ is a pain.

3 An _____ is when a sound bounces back.

4 _____ is where we go to learn.

5 Every ship has an _____.

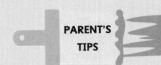 PARENT'S TIPS — Help your child to read all the 'ch' words once they have been completed, before attempting to use them to finish the sentences.

25

Join the letters to make the word.

Read the word. Hear the letter sounds.

sing · ing

singing

Join the letters to make the words.

mix · ing   fly · ing   eat · ing

_____   _____   _____

Label the pictures correctly.

_____   _____   _____

Join the letters to make the words and write them below. Draw a picture in the boxes.

_____   _____   _____

jump · ing   cry · ing   read · ing

PARENT'S TIPS

Before working this page play at miming certain actions (e.g. cooking, ironing, etc) and ask your child to guess what you are doing. All the words used should end with 'ing'.

Each person likes doing the thing beginn**ing** with the same letter as their name. What does each person like do**ing**?

Amy   Ben   Cara   Dan   Emma   Frank

cook   eat   act   fish   build   draw

Write a sentence about each person. Draw a picture.

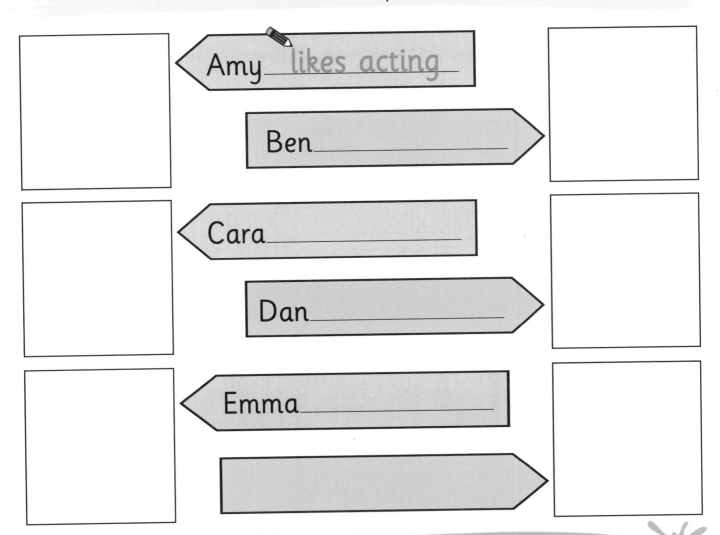

Amy ___likes acting___

Ben _____

Cara _____

Dan _____

Emma _____

_____

Join the letters to make the word.

Read the word. Hear the letter sounds.

star s

stars

Join the letters to make the words.

toy s

mask s

coin s

_____   _____   _____

Label the pictures correctly.

_____   _____   _____

Join the letters to make the words and write them below. Draw a picture in the boxes.

_____   _____   _____

hook s

cloud s

clown s

28

PARENT'S TIPS

Many plurals end with 's'. Look round the home and count up things whose names take 's' in the plural e.g. six cups, four chairs, etc.

- s - s - s - s - s - s - s - s - s - s - s - s - s - s

Write the missing words.

one	two
one apple	two _apples_
one bird	two _____
one car	two _____
one duck	two _____
one egg	two _____
one _____	two frogs
one _____	two girls
one _____	two hats
one _____	two insects
one _____	two jugs

PARENT'S TIPS Notice how each word is made plural by adding 's' to the end of it.

29

Join the letters to make the word.

Read the word. Hear the letter sounds.

fox **es**

fox**es**

Join the letters to make the words.

bus **es**

bush **es**

arch **es**

_____

_____

_____

Label the pictures correctly.

_____

_____

_____

Join the letters to make the words and write them below. Draw a picture in the boxes.

_____

_____

_____

box **es**

glass **es**

brush **es**

30

PARENT'S TIPS

Some words take 'es' in the plural (words ending with 's', 'x', 'ch' or 'sh'). Read the words with your child and point this out.

- Play this game with a partner.
- You need a dice and some pencils.
- Each person must choose a different set.
- Take it in turns to throw the dice.
- Colour in the correct picture for each number you throw.
- The first person to colour in all six pictures is the winner.

Set A

1 one glass

2 two dish**es**

3 three bench**es**

4 four fox**es**

5 five arch**es**

6 six six**es**

Set B

6 six peach**es**

5 five bush**es**

4 four box**es**

3 three torch**es**

2 two brush**es**

1 one bus

PARENT'S TIPS — Each time the dice is thrown, ask your child to read the word the number refers to.

31

Count the objects. Fill in the missing words.

one bus

three buses

one glass

_____

one fox

_____

one box

_____

one church

_____

one watch

_____

one peach

_____

one dish

_____

one bush

_____

one brush

_____

Ask your child to count the different pictures and complete the
answers. Ensure your child remembers to use the 'es' ending.